P9-DBV-203

THE REAL
MOTHER GOOSE®
Piano Book

Illustrated by
Blanche Fisher Wright

CHECKERBOARD PRESS ❖ NEW YORK

Mary Had A Little Lamb

| 10 | 9 | 8 | 9 | 10 | 10 | 10 | 9 | 9 | 9 | 10 | 12 | 12 |
| Mar - | y | had | a | lit - | tle | lamb, | Lit - | tle | lamb, | Lit - | tle | lamb, |

| 10 | 9 | 8 | 9 | 10 | 10 | 10 | 10 | 9 | 9 | 10 | 9 | 8 |
| Mar - | y | had | a | lit - | tle | lamb, | Its | fleece | was | white | as | snow. |

Baa, Baa Black Sheep

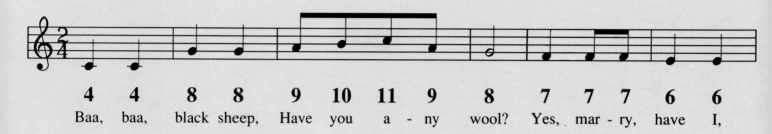

4 4 8 8 9 10 11 9 8 7 7 7 6 6

Baa, baa, black sheep, Have you a - ny wool? Yes, mar - ry, have I,

5 5 4 8 8 8 7 7 6 6 6

Three bags full; One for my mas - ter, one for my

5 5 8 8 8 7 8 9 7 6 5 5 4

dame, But none for the lit - tle boy Who cries in the lane.

Humpty Dumpty

4 6 5 7   6 7 8 9   4 6 5 7

Hump – ty Dump – ty   sat on a wall, Hump – ty Dump – ty

6 4 2 4   4 4 6 5 5 7

had a great fall;   All the King's hor – ses, and

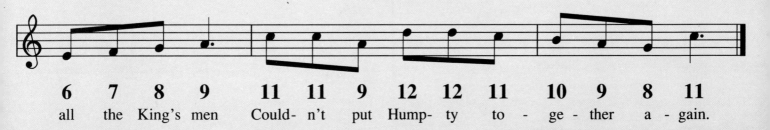

6 7 8 9   11 11 9 12 12 11 10 9 8 11

all the King's men Could– n't put Hump– ty to – ge – ther a – gain.

Hot Cross Buns

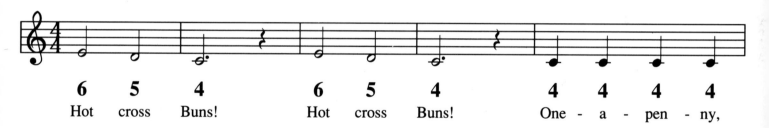

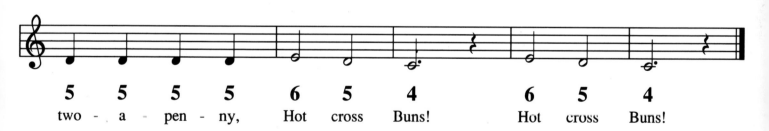

Sing A Song of Sixpence

8　9　8　6　4　11　11　10　10　5　6　7　7　8　7　5

Sing　a　song　of　six - pence,　A　poc - ket　full　of　rye;　Four - and- twen - ty

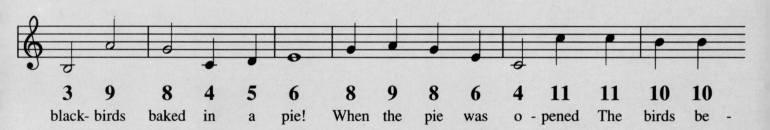

3　9　8　4　5　6　8　9　8　6　4　11　11　10　10

black- birds　baked　in　a　pie!　When　the　pie　was　o - pened　The　birds　be -

5　6　7　7　8　9　8　7　6　5　6　7　8　9　10　11

gan　to　sing;　Was　not　that　a　dain - ty　dish　To　set　be - fore　the　king?

The Cat and the Fiddle

6 6 6 6 7 8   5 5 5 5 6 7

Hey, did – dle did – dle! The cat and the fid – dle, The

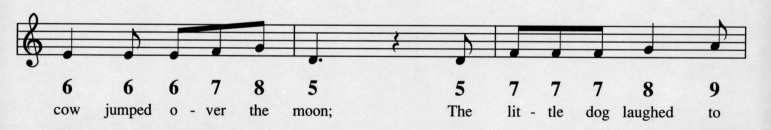

6 6 6 7 8 5   5 7 7 7 8 9

cow jumped o - ver the moon; The lit - tle dog laughed to

8 7 6 6 6 5 5 5 5 4 5 4

see such sport, And the dish ran a - way with the spoon.

Three Blind Mice

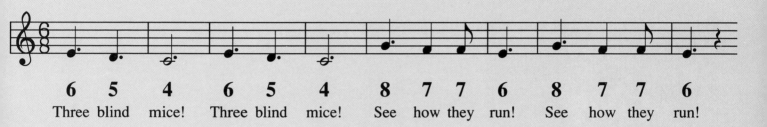

6	5	4	6	5	4	8	7	7	6	8	7	7	6
Three	blind	mice!	Three	blind	mice!	See	how	they	run!	See	how	they	run!

8	11	11	10	9	10	11	8	8	8	11	11	11	10	9	10
They	all	ran	af -	ter	the	far -	mer's	wife,	Who	cut	off	their	tails	with	a

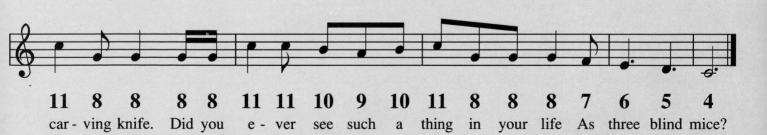

11	8	8	8	8	11	11	10	9	10	11	8	8	8	7	6	5	4
car -	ving	knife.	Did	you	e -	ver	see	such	a	thing	in	your	life	As	three	blind	mice?

Jack and Jill

7 4 5 4 7 4 5 4 9 8 7 6 5 4

Jack and Jill went up the hill, To fetch a pail of wa - ter;

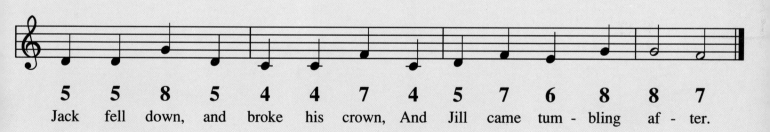

5 5 8 5 4 4 7 4 5 7 6 8 8 7

Jack fell down, and broke his crown, And Jill came tum - bling af - ter.

Hickory, Dickory Dock

6	7	8	8	9	10	11		6
Hick -	or -	y	dick -	or -	y	dock!		The

6	7	8	8	9	10	11		8	11	11	10	10
mouse	ran	up		the	clock;			The	clock	struck	one,	And

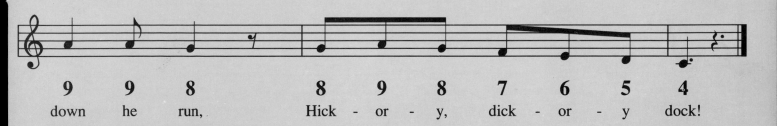

9	9	8		8	9	8	7	6	5	4
down	he	run,		Hick -	or -	y,	dick -	or -	y	dock!